DR. PREN
AND THE DAYS OF HIS CHILDHOOD

....

MÁXIMO CÉSAR CASTELLANOS

EDITORIAL RAMY

Georgetown, Delaware

Editorial Ramy
Georgetown, Delaware

Publisher's Note: This is a work of fiction. Names, characters, places, and incidents are a product of the author's imagination. Public names and places are sometimes used for atmospheric purposes. Any resemblance to actual people, living or dead, or to businesses, companies, events, institutions, or places is completely coincidental.

Book Layout © BookDesignTemplates.com
Cover designed by Rafido

DR. PREN AND THE DAYS OF HIS CHILDHOOD / Máximo César Castellanos.
First Edition, 2020
ISBN 978-0-578-72818-6
Printed in the United States of America

Contents

This book is dedicated to Sister Ascensión,

Sister Francisca, Sister María, and Sister Rosa

for all their encouragement and support.

"Treat others the way

you want to be treated."

CHAPTER ONE

....

THE BET

In the beginning, everything was brown. The brown took the form of a shoe. The shoe was worn by a man. The man was sitting in a chair inside a cabin. The man mysteriously appeared one day. Nobody knew anything about him.

It was a hot day in South Carolina in a small town near the beach called Pascanwon. A young man was walking down the street, going to his job. The young man worked in a bar. The young man was George.

Upon reaching the bar, George entered and felt the humid air. George opened the windows to let in the fresh air. George grabbed a broom and started to sweep the floor.

"Clean it well because Don Ponanso is coming today," said his boss.

"So what? It's not like he is the owner of half of this city," said George.

"That's exactly who he is. He is a billionaire and the owner of half of this city. He made all his fortune by winning bets. He is an excellent poker player and has beaten many rich people," said his boss.

"So then, is he going to come here?" asked George.

"Of course, he is. He sent me a letter telling me he was coming today," said his boss and he left.

"He only tells me that, so that the place is clean. That Don Ponanso probably won't even arrive," said George to himself.

George cleaned all day, but no one came. At dusk, the door to the bar opened, and a man in a white suit entered. The man had six bodyguards with him. The man had shoes and a hat made entirely out of gold. The man was Don Ponanso.

"It is an honor to have you here. Would you like some whiskey?" asked the boss as Don Ponanso sat down.

"How is it going with the Pren guy?" asked Don Ponanso while the boss was returning with some glasses with whiskey.

"Like always, nothing new," said the boss.

"Do you think he is dead?" asked Don Ponanso.

"Of course not. Somebody in the cabin is still using a lot of electricity. That's why I think he is not dead," said the boss.

"Who are you talking about?" asked George.

"You be quiet," his boss told him.

"Leave him alone. He is just being curious. I don't blame him. If I was him, I would also be curious to know who we are talking about," said Don Ponanso.

"Boy, 30 years ago, a man called Dr. Pren came to this town. He asked your boss here if he had a cabin with electricity available for rent. Apparently, this was exactly what your boss had. The cabin across the street is the one that your boss rented to that Pren. He has not come out one single time since he moved there 30 years ago," said Don Ponanso.

"Is he dead?" asked George.

"I pay the electricity of the cabin, and it seems he is still using a lot of electricity. That's why I think he is not dead," said his boss.

"But then, how does he get food? Why does he need so much electricity?" asked George.

"I don't know, but maybe you should go there and ask him," said Don Ponanso.

"Why don't you ask him?" asked George.

"Do you want to bet to see who goes there to ask him?" asked Don Ponanso.

"No, I am not interested. I have no need to bet," said George.

"Never mind that, let's solve this with a game of poker. The loser has to go to the cabin and ask Pren to tell him everything

DR. PREN AND THE DAYS OF HIS CHILDHOOD

about his life. If he doesn't do it, the loser will pay with his life," said Don Ponanso.

"But I don't know how to play poker," said George.

"I'll take that as a yes. Okay? Fabulous. Let's get started," said Don Ponanso.

"But . . ." said George.

Don Ponanso began to deal the cards.

"What happens if Dr. Pren is actually dead?" asked George.

"Well, anyway, the loser will pay with his life," said Don Ponanso.

After just a few minutes, George lost.

"Goodbye, cruel world," whispered George.

"Well loser, to show you that I am not that mean, I will give you until Saturday to figure out everything about Pren's life," said Don Ponanso.

"But that's only five days. I don't think I can figure out everything about his life in such a short time," said George.

"Then, don't waste any time. Hurry up!" exclaimed Don Ponanso.

George stood up and left the bar like a lightning bolt. George crossed the street and knocked on the door of the little cabin, but nobody answered.

Suddenly, the door opened. A man with brown hair was inside the cabin sitting in a chair. The man was Dr. Pren. George entered the cabin and looked behind the door to see who had opened it. But the only thing he saw behind the door was a cable lying on the floor.

"Leave. I don't want to see anybody," said Dr. Pren.

"Are you Dr. Pren?" asked George.

"How do you know my name?" asked Dr. Pren.

"Don Ponanso told me," said George.

"What do you want?" asked Dr. Pren.

"I lost a bet, and if you don't tell me everything about your life, things won't end very well for me," said George.

Dr. Pren was silent for a few seconds.

"I wouldn't want to be the cause of a tragedy. Please, take a seat," said Dr. Pren.

So, George walked towards a chair that was next to Dr. Pren and sat down.

Dr. Pren began telling George his life story. *It all started a long, long, long time ago . . .*

CHAPTER TWO

....

THE MOVIE THEATER

I lived on a small farm in Florida. I lived with Mr. and Mrs. Thups. When I was a baby, they found me in a cardboard box on the front step of their house. In the box, there was a note that said that I was one year old. The note stated that I should not be registered so that my existence would never be known. So, Mr. and Mrs. Thups did not tell anybody about me. For that reason, I do not have a birth certificate, and I never went to school. It was as if I did not exist.

Mr. and Mrs. Thups did not give me a name. They decided that when I could speak, I could give myself a name. I chose my name and called myself Dr. Pren.

When I turned 5 years old, Mr. Thups got a new job in a city in Florida called Vesnam, a few hours north of the farm. We moved to a neighborhood called Donstown, which was a few minutes outside the city of Vesnam.

Living in a neighborhood was very different than living on a farm. I missed all the animals on the farm. Mrs. Thups offered to buy me a puppy, but I didn't want that type of pet. I wasn't sure what type of pet I wanted either, so Mrs. Thups gave me an idea. She told me that maybe I could create my own pet. Her idea got me so excited. Ever since that day, I have worked hard to create my own pet. Unfortunately, during the first year of work, I couldn't bring something to life even for one second.

I worked every day except Saturdays because that was the only day that Ben and I could play. Ben Abioye was a boy who lived in the neighborhood. I met Ben the day after I moved there.

One day, I was sitting with Ben under a tree in his backyard, eating an apple.

"What do you want to do today?" I asked.

"How about we go to the movie theater?" he suggested.

"What is a movie theater?" I asked.

"A movie theater is a place where you see movies on a giant screen," said Ben.

"I didn't understand anything that you just told me," I said.

"It doesn't matter. When we get there, you are going to have fun," said Ben.

Ben went into his garage and got out two bicycles.

"Here. This is my dad's, but he never uses it," said Ben as he gave me the bicycle.

We got on the bicycles and rode to the city. Finally, we got to the movie theater. We went into the movie theater and started to walk towards one of the theaters when suddenly, a woman stopped us.

"You need a ticket to enter the theater," said the woman.

"Where do we get a ticket?" asked Ben.

"There in the ticket booth," said the woman.

So, Ben and I walked towards the ticket booth and stood in front of it. A man was inside the ticket booth.

"Can you give us two tickets?" I asked the man.

"Do you have money?" asked the man.

"No," I answered.

"Then, scram," said the man.

"But we want to see the movie," said Ben.

"You need money to buy tickets," said the man.

"So, scram or I'll call your parents," said the man.

"And how are you going to do that if you don't know who my parents are?" asked Ben.

The man got mad. He came out of the ticket booth, grabbed us by the shirts, and threw us in the trash can.

"This is child abuse! I am going to call the police!" screamed Ben from the trash can.

"Do you know the police's telephone number?" I asked.

"I have no idea, but I told him that so he would leave us alone," said Ben.

We climbed out of the trash can and went back to the neighborhood. When I got home, I smelled so bad that I stunk up the whole house. Mrs. Thups got so mad, she punished me. I couldn't leave my room for a week.

When I could finally leave my room, I went to play with Ben.

When I got to Ben's backyard, there was another boy with Ben. The boy had blue hands and very long fingernails. He appeared to be my age.

"Hello Dr. Pren. While you were punished, a new kid moved to the neighborhood. His name is Adam," said Ben.

"Hello," I said.

"Hello. Do you want to go to the movie theater?" Adam asked me.

"I don't want to get in trouble again," I said.

"I understand that, but look at what I have," said Adam, as he took some coins out of his pocket.

"Where did you get them?" I asked.

"From my mother's purse. The man said you needed money, well, here you have it," said Adam.

So, we returned to the movie theater. When we stood in front of the ticket booth, Adam took out his coins.

"I want three tickets," said Adam.

"You only have 45 cents here and you need 30 dollars to buy three tickets," said the man.

"Do you know how long it took me to collect this money?" asked Adam.

"Let me guess, a second?" asked the man.

Adam glared at the man. His face turned red. Then, Adam decided to sneak into the movie theater. Ben and I followed him. We entered one of the movie theaters. We were about to sit down when the man captured us and kicked us out of the movie theater.

"I am going to take you home so I can tell your parents what you have done," said the man.

"Of course you won't do that because I won't tell you where I live. My friends don't even know where I live," said Ben.

"Yes, I do. You live in the first house on the left in the Donstown neighborhood," said Adam.

Ben looked at Adam with a mad look on his face. The man grabbed us by our shirts and brought us to Ben's house.

When we got to Ben's house, the man started to tell Ben's parents everything that had happened. While he was talking, I sneaked over to my house and hid in my room for the rest of the day.

The next week, I went to Ben's house, but he wasn't there. Every time Ben misbehaved, his mother sent him to stay with a man, who was very strict, so he could teach Ben good manners.

"Can you tell me where Ben is?" I asked.

"Ben is at the house at the end of the Seaside neighborhood," said Ben's mom.

I immediately went running towards the Seaside neighborhood. When I arrived at the house, Ben was running towards me as if a monster was chasing him.

"What's going on?" I asked Ben as he ran past me.

"The dog!" screamed Ben.

Suddenly, a giant 30-foot-tall dog jumped in the air and landed on the house, smashing it into pieces. Seeing this, I ran as fast as I could to catch up to Ben.

CHAPTER THREE

....

THE ROOM OF MADNESS

*"W*hat's going on?" I screamed.*

"I didn't know, but the man who taught me good manners is also a scientist. I think he is a crazy scientist because he created a formula to alter the atoms of living things. The first living thing he tried his formula on was his dog. When he tried it for the first time, nothing happened to the dog. He thought that the formula had failed, so he threw the formula in his garden. The formula expanded everywhere, invading the plants that were around his house," said Ben.

"Does that mean what happened to the dog is also going to happen to the plants around his house?" I asked.

"You mean to say something already happened to the plants. The plants transformed into little bugs. Anything they bite transforms into more bugs," said Ben.

We didn't know where to go, so we decided to go to Adam's house.

Adam was in his room when we got there. His house was somewhat peculiar. The curiosity to explore his house invaded both of us. This was especially true when we got to a room that had a sign that said 'Room of Madness.'

"You can enter if you want," said Adam.

Ben and I completely forgot what was happening outside the house, and we entered the 'Room of Madness' excitedly.

When we entered the room, there was hardly any light. Suddenly, I noticed what seemed to be some jail cell bars. I didn't feel comfortable, so I turned around to leave the room. But, when I turned around, I noticed that the door and Ben had

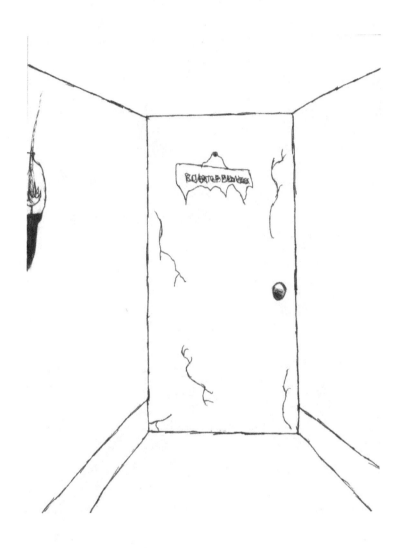

disappeared. I looked towards the ceiling. The ceiling looked like the inside of a safe. I looked down, looked around, and realized that I was actually inside a giant safe.

Suddenly, the safe started to shrink. Water began to enter under the door and started to fill the safe. It got darker and darker inside the safe.

"You have no escape," said a scary voice.

I didn't know where the voice came from. The safe was now so small that it was crushing me. The safe was almost completely full of water, and it was so dark inside there that I could hardly see anything.

"All alone, with no one to help you," said the scary voice.

When finally, the safe was full of water and it got completely dark inside, the safe stopped crushing me. Now, I could stretch my body completely and move easily from one side to another. I started to swim up in search of air. Luckily, I managed to get my head above water before drowning. I saw where I was. I was in the middle of the ocean at night. There was no beach near me.

"No help," said the scary voice.

Suddenly, something sucked me under the water. Then, I appeared inside a tube, traveling at an incredibly fast speed. Immediately after, I flew out of the tube and landed on my feet on a street in a city.

At that moment, a hand grabbed my shoulder. I turned around and saw a kid with blue hands. One of his eyes looked like the eye of a snake while his hair covered the other eye.

"Everything is your fault," said the kid.

Then, I noticed that the scary voice came from the kid. I closed my eyes and started screaming. When I opened my eyes, I found myself back in Adam's house. Ben and Adam were next to me.

"What was all that?" I asked.

"That is a room that my dad built to capture intruders. It causes optical illusions based on your worst fears. It makes you more and more insane until your head explodes, literally," said Adam.

"Sometimes, the room shows visions of what your worst fears will be. What did you see?" asked Adam.

"Well, I saw that . . ." I started to say when I noticed that Adam's hairstyle was the same as the kid in my vision.

Then, I screamed and started to move away from him.

"What happened to your hair?" I asked.

"It's just that, while you were in the room, I got bored and decided to change my hairstyle. Do you like it?" Adam asked me.

"I asked you what happened, because in my vision, I saw a kid who was tormenting me, and he had that same hairstyle," I said.

"But you know that I would never do that. You and Ben are my best friends. I would even sacrifice my life for you guys," said Adam.

"You are right," I said.

"It was a bad idea to go into that room, right?" I asked.

"Of course, it was," said Ben.

"How about we forget this," said Adam.

"You are right," said Ben.

Suddenly, someone knocked on the front door.

CHAPTER FOUR

....

GREGORY MCBARN

We went to see who it was. When we opened the front door, we met an old man.

"What are you doing there? The world needs you!" exclaimed the old man.

"What are you talking about?" I asked.

"There are bugs everywhere. I am trying to recruit people to help me finish them off," said the old man.

"Hey, old man, stop joking," said Adam.

Then, Ben whispered to Adam that the bugs were real.

"Pardon me, my dear old humble man," said Adam.

"Are you going to help me? Because I don't have all day," said the old man.

"Fine, we will help you," said Ben.

"Exactly how are we going to finish off those bugs, Dumbledore?" asked Adam.

"My name is Gregory McBarn!" exclaimed the old man.

"Mr. McBorn, is anyone else going to help us?" asked Ben.

"My last name is McBarn. There is another house where we can go to ask for help," said Gregory.

Then, we crossed the street and went towards the house in front. A man opened the door.

"Sir, what are you doing standing there? The future of the world is in your hands," said Gregory.

"Wait a second, Dumbledore," said the man and he went towards the kitchen.

When he came back, he was carrying a beer in his hand.

"Now, you can continue with your dramatic speech," said the man.

"Sir, you appear to be someone capable of saving the world. Your face shows that you are ready to do it. You face shows that . . . that . . . What is happening to your face?" asked Gregory.

The man's face looked to be collapsing. Suddenly, the man transformed into a bunch of bugs. Then, the entire house transformed into a bunch of bugs. I saw a bug bite the bottle of beer. Immediately, the bottle of beer transformed into a bunch of bugs.

We all ran away immediately.

When we thought that we had lost them, we hid behind a bush.

"How are we supposed to get rid of those bugs? Anything they bite transforms into more bugs! Whatever weapon we use would be useless against them!" I screamed.

"That's why I brought us all together to use our brilliant minds to invent something that will destroy them," said Gregory.

"That is your grand plan!" I screamed desperately.

"Calm down," said Gregory.

"I am not going to calm down! Your plan is stupid! We are all going to die!" I screamed.

"I think I am having a panic attack," I said.

"If you don't like my plan, you tell us what to do," said Gregory.

At that moment, I had the most brilliant idea of all.

"How about if we use our brilliant minds to invent something," I suggested.

"That is exactly what I just said!" screamed Gregory.

"Hey, calm down, my friend. No need to get furious," I told him.

"How about we create a formula to counter the transformative effects of the bugs?" asked Ben.

"That doesn't sound bad," I said.

"What are you saying? That is exactly what we need," said Gregory.

"Yes, but to do that, we need a little bit of the original formula that created those bugs, and there is none left," said Ben.

"I think I know where we can find some of the formula," said Gregory.

"I am a train conductor. Yesterday, my train broke down, not very far from here. Suddenly, a very peculiar looking man came out of nowhere and helped me repair the train. The man had a jar with him that contained a liquid that was swirling like a tornado and had bubbles on the bottom, which seemed strange to me. Once the man repaired the train, he left without me realizing, but I noticed that he had forgotten the jar containing the liquid. Maybe that is the formula that you are talking about," said Gregory.

Then, we headed towards the train station. When we got there, I looked through one of the windows of the train car, and I could see a lot of bugs surrounding a jar on a table next to the window. I put my hand through the window and grabbed the jar without any of the bugs noticing.

When I pulled my hand out, I noticed that I had taken out a jar full of oil. I returned the jar to its place and saw another jar on top of another table in the locomotive. I did not want to make the same mistake, so I asked Gregory what color the formula was.

"It was red and seemed to have some branches coming out of it," said Gregory.

I looked at the jar again. The jar seemed to contain exactly what Gregory had just described.

"How am I going to grab the jar without the bugs seeing me?" I asked Adam.

"Leave it to me," said Adam.

Adam grabbed a rock and stood at the entrance of the train station. Adam threw the rock towards the other end of the train station. When the rock crashed against the ground, the bugs turned to look at the rock.

"The bugs will head towards the rock, and then we can escape," said Adam.

Suddenly, all the bugs turned towards Adam and headed towards him.

"Or maybe the bugs are more intelligent than what I thought, and they will go after the person who threw the rock. Goodbye," said Adam.

Adam took off running as fast as he could while an army of bugs chased after him. When I looked through the window of the locomotive again, the jar was still there on the table, but there weren't any more bugs near the jar. Gregory, Ben, and I entered the locomotive. Gregory grabbed the jar.

"How can we be sure that this is the formula that we need?" I asked.

"There is only one way to find out," said Gregory.

Gregory poured a few drops on the locomotive. The train started to slowly move towards the gate that gave access to the train.

"We are going to crash," I told Gregory.

"Don't be afraid. At this speed, we won't feel hardly anything," said Gregory.

Right before we crashed into the gate, the train stopped. Nothing happened for a few seconds.

"This is not the formula," I shouted.

Suddenly, the train took off full speed ahead faster than a bullet. The train crashed into the gate, breaking it into pieces. The train was going so fast that it was leaving fire on the tracks. Gregory, Ben, and I were holding on to the conductor's chair so that we would not fly out of the locomotive.

The train kept on moving forward. We were now in the middle of the street, moving towards a traffic jam. The train crashed into the cars. Cars were flying everywhere.

Suddenly, I slipped and began to fly out of the locomotive, but Gregory caught me. Then, Ben slipped, and Gregory caught him with his other hand. Immediately, we realized that Gregory was not holding onto the conductor's chair any longer. The three of us went flying out of the locomotive.

We landed on the grass on the side of the road. As we stood up, we saw the train disappear in the distance.

Suddenly, I heard a voice behind me.

"I've been looking for you, Dr. Pren," said the voice.

When I turned around, I couldn't believe what I was seeing.

CHAPTER FIVE

....

THE CUBES OF TIME

*R*ight behind me was Adam.

"Are you the spirit of Adam?" I asked.

"Of course not, I am Adam. The bugs stopped coming after me when they saw a train conductor arrive at the train station. That allowed me to escape," said Adam.

"That's good!" I said.

"Do you have the formula?" asked Adam.

"Here it is," said Gregory taking the jar out of his pocket.

"Where can we go to experiment with the formula," asked Ben.

"We can go to my house," said Adam.

We ran off to Adam's house. When we arrived at his house, we didn't know what to do with the formula, so I did the first thing that came to my mind. I grabbed all of the medicines that were in the medicine cabinet and threw them into the formula.

"What are you doing?" asked Gregory.

"Do you think I know?" I asked.

I walked through the house, looking everywhere. I went into a room and found some shiny yellow cubes.

"This is the forbidden room," said Adam as I entered the room.

"I am not allowed to go in," said Adam.

"But I have not been prohibited from entering the room," I said.

"You are right," said Adam.

"Are these cubes important?" I asked.

"I don't know. I have never seen them before," said Adam.

I grabbed the cubes and tried to put them into the jar, but they were too big.

Suddenly, the cubes shrank. I had already seen enough strange things that day. For that reason, it didn't surprise me to see the cubes shrink. I put the cubes into the jar, and they sunk into the formula.

Some green symbols appeared around the jar, and suddenly, the symbols began to change into words. The words were written in English. The words formed sentences that said, "You have just transferred the 'Cubes of Time' to this formula which will cause the formula to have unexpected effects."

Gregory read what it said because none of us knew how to read yet.

"Once, my mom told me a tale about a king who used some cubes called the 'Cubes of Time' to travel to the past to visit family members who had died," said Ben.

"Do you think these are those 'Cubes of Time'?" I asked.

"Of course not. That is only a fairy tale," said Ben.

"What if the story is real?" I asked.

"I don't know, but to me, it all seems fake," said Ben.

"But what if it is real," said Adam.

"Adam, if these cubes are somehow the 'Cubes of Time', how is it that your parents got them?" asked Gregory.

"How am I supposed to know that? I have never seen them before," said Adam.

"At the end of the story, the king gave the 'Cubes of Time' to his daughter, who later married a prince. I think the prince's name was Samuel Hopper," said Ben.

"Hopper?" asked Adam.

"Yes. Do you know anyone with that last name?" asked Ben.

"Of course, I do. That is my last name," said Adam.

"Do you think the 'Cubes of Time' may have been passed down from generation to generation until they got to your parents?" asked Gregory.

"No. I just think it is a strange coincidence," said Adam.

41

"I believe Adam is correct. All this is just pure coincidence and doesn't mean anything," said Ben.

"You are right, not all fairy tales are real," said Gregory.

It was three against one, so I had no choice but to drop the subject.

Suddenly, out of nowhere, the train went right through the wall of the house. Everyone was able to get out of the way. The train destroyed everything that was in its path.

Gregory grabbed the jar and put it in his pocket.

After the train had left, we noticed that the train had split the house in half.

"I hope that your parents have insurance," Gregory said to Adam.

Suddenly, we heard a roar.

"Now what?" asked Gregory.

Then, the giant 30-foot-tall dog jumped on one half of the house, destroying it in the process. Adam jumped on one of the dog's legs, slid under the paw, and went into the debris. Adam was in what used to be his room. Adam started looking for his water guns. Finally, he found an empty water gun made out of plastic and metal.

At that moment, Gregory noticed that he no longer had the jar with the new formula in his pocket. Then, he saw that Adam had the formula and was pouring a little bit of the formula into the water gun.

Suddenly, the dog grabbed Adam by his jacket with his mouth and lifted him into the air. Adam shot one of the dog's paws. Immediately, the dog let go of him. Suddenly, the dog's paw turned into ashes.

"It works," screamed Adam.

Adam continued shooting the dog until the entire dog turned into ashes.

"We did it! We did it!" screamed Gregory as everyone ran towards Adam.

In that instant, Adam slipped and shot one of the windows of his house. The window immediately turned into ashes.

"Fabulous, it works on anything!" screamed Ben.

Then, Adam shot a tree just to prove that, in reality, it would work on anything. The tree turned into ashes.

"With this, nothing can get in our way," I said.

Or at least that is what I thought . . .

Then, we went to destroy the bugs. When we got to where they were, we saw some of the bugs biting some trees, turning them into bugs. Adam was about to shoot them when the water gun started to break.

So, I made my calculations quickly and concluded that the water gun needed to be more resistant and the formula needed more heat and more mass. Well, maybe I exaggerated a little. Actually, I didn't have any idea what I was doing. I didn't even know what the word mass meant. But at least, I knew that we were going to need more formula. I grabbed a bucket of hot water and added it to the formula that was in the water gun.

Suddenly, the formula started to vanish until there was only one drop of formula left in the water gun.

Then, I grabbed a piece of grass and put it in the water gun. I didn't have any idea what I was doing. I just did the first thing that came to my mind. The drop of formula absorbed the grass and caused an unexpected reaction. The water gun filled with the formula and it was now much more resistant than before.

"You are a genius," whispered Adam.

"I know," I said.

"You are brilliant," said Gregory.

"Obviously," I said.

"But what did you do?" Ben asked me.

Actually, I had no idea. I lied so that I would not look like a fool.

"It is known as 'The Volvion Paradox.' It is when weird things happen, and you have to do weird things so that weird things do not keep happening," I said.

"What? I didn't understand anything," said Ben.

The truth is that I understood even less, but I would look even dumber if I told them the truth, so I lied again.

"This is highly advanced science. You would understand even less if I tried to explain it to you," I told them.

"We have already talked a lot. Let's destroy those bugs," said Gregory.

But the bugs had already found us. A bug was standing right in front of us. When we all looked at it, the bug bit the pavement.

Suddenly, the ground started to shake. The pavement began to transform into bugs. Then, all the streets started to transform into bugs.

"This is not good," said Gregory as we turned to look towards the center of the city.

Right away, we saw that all the buildings were vanishing.

"We won't be able to destroy them if they keep creating more bugs," said Adam.

"It is even less likely that we will be able to destroy them if they succeed in transforming the entire planet into bugs," said Ben.

Suddenly, the water gun started to break again.

"Maybe the material that the water gun is made up of is not strong enough," I said.

In that instant, we were surrounded by a bunch of bugs.

CHAPTER SIX

....

THE SEARCH

*E*verything seemed to be lost. We were sure that this would be the end. When out of nowhere, the end of a rope fell on my head.

I looked up and saw a girl in a tree holding the other end of the rope. Ben, Adam, Gregory, and I grabbed onto the rope. The girl pulled the rope and lifted us onto the tree. Immediately, the girl led us inside a house that was next to the tree. The bugs never saw us enter the house.

"Thank you," Ben said to the girl.

The girl was tall with yellow hair and wore motorcycle goggles.

"I know how to fix your water gun," said the girl.

"Where are we?" asked Gregory.

"This is my aunt's house. Right now, she is on vacation. My name is Alice," said the girl.

Alice brought us to the kitchen. In the kitchen, Alice got out a bunch of jars from a cabinet. When I opened the water gun, a cloud of smoke came out of it and filled the room with smoke. When the smoke dissipated, Alice examined the formula.

"Where did you get this?" asked Alice.

"I created it," I said.

"You? You seem like you can't even tell a rooster from a hen," said Alice.

"Whoever created this must be a genius! The particles of this formula are bonded in such a way that they create molecules that I have never seen before in my life," said Alice.

"How do you know this?" asked Gregory.

"I installed a mini microscope of very advanced technology on my glasses," said Alice.

"I don't believe you," said Adam.

"I am an inventor," said Alice.

"Well, can you tell us how to fix the water gun?" asked Ben.

"Wait a moment. I need to analyze the formula and its effects on the structure of the water gun," said Alice.

Alice grabbed a metal spoon, a glass jar, and a wooden plate. Alice added each one of them to the formula. The spoon, the jar, and the plate were destroyed when they came into contact with the formula.

"It seems that the formula destroys everything it touches. The fact that it does not completely destroy the water gun means that the water gun is made out of molecules that are resistant and sensitive to the effects of the formula. We need to experiment with each molecule that makes up the water gun's structure to find out which is the resistant molecule. Then, we will create a new weapon using only the molecules resistant to the formula," said Alice.

"Could you repeat that? I stopped listening after you said the formula destroys everything it touches," I said.

"You must be joking," said Alice.

"I am not joking. It's true," I said.

Alice separated the molecules that formed the structure of one part of the water gun and added a drop of formula to each molecule. The plastic molecules were the only molecules that didn't get destroyed when they came in contact with the formula.

"Perfect, the new weapon will be made out of only plastic," said Alice.

Alice grabbed all of the plastic that there was in the house and built some crossbows. The crossbows shot arrows that had chambers in the arrowhead, which contained the formula. She gave a crossbow to each one of us.

Once we were prepared, we walked out of the garage dramatically. Obviously, I was in the middle of the group. We walked as if *we were moving in slow motion. As we left the garage, we started shooting arrows at all the bugs that got in our way. It was easy to destroy them. The bugs didn't stand a chance against our new weapons.*

Soon, I noticed that many bugs had disappeared.

"Do you think they gave up?" asked Ben.

"I don't think so. I feel that there are still a lot of them out there, and they are not going to give up, just like that," I said.

"I think you are right," said Ben.

Suddenly, something started to emerge in the distance. A shadow began to cover the sunny sky. Then, a pupil millions of times the size of my pupil appeared in the shadow.

"That is really big," I said.

"Do you think so?" asked Adam.

"The pupil looks a little bit blurry," said Alice.

I looked at the pupil, and then I noticed an entire eye. Soon after, I noticed a whole head was forming. The head was black with four eyes and had spikes all over the face. Then, I saw a bug flying in the air towards the head.

Apparently, all the bugs were gathering together and creating what appeared to be a gigantic monster.

The monster was incredibly big. So big that its head was the size of planet earth. The monster floated in space and looked at planet earth while it was being created. The monster was being created at an incredibly fast speed.

"Ben, I don't understand how your mom's friend could have created that," I said.

"Mən Xephermous," said the monster.

The monster had a giant mouth, so when it spoke, it made a sound so loud that I thought my ears were going to explode.

"Jag är den Xephermous," said the monster.

"What is it saying?" I asked Gregory.

"I have no idea," said Gregory.

"Ik ben de Xephermous," said the monster.

"Maybe it is talking to us in its own language," said Ben.

"Eu sou o Xephermous," said the monster.

"I recognize that language. The other day, there was a man in the store who said 'eu sou o,'" said Ben.

"I am Xephermous," said the monster.

"I understand now. It is saying who it is in different languages so that the whole world will understand it," said Gregory.

Gregory was right. We listened to the same phrase in different languages for the next few minutes. Finally, after a few minutes, it started to say something different. When it said it in English, this is what we heard.

"I will build a paradise on your planet just for me. I will destroy you all," said Xephermous.

"That is not good, right?" I asked Adam.

"Of course not," said Adam.

"Well, at least we tried. If you are looking for me, I will be in my house eating my last cookies," said Gregory as he put his weapon on the ground.

"We can't give up so easily," I said to them.

Seconds later . . . I was alone in the middle of the street, holding everyone's weapons.

"Or maybe we can," I said.

Then, I attacked Xephermous, but every time I shot an arrow, gravity just pulled the arrow straight down to the ground.

Finally, I gave up. I walked towards the city, or what was left of it. I passed by the movie theater.

"Stupid movie theater! This is all your fault!" I exclaimed.

Without looking where I was going, I crashed into a trash can.

"Get out of my way," I said while I kicked the trash can.

When the trash can fell on the ground, some big plastic tubes fell out onto the ground.

When I saw the tubes, a great idea came to my mind. I remembered what the water gun looked like when Alice took it apart to examine it. I used the same mechanism as a blueprint to build some giant plastic cannons that could shoot the formula great distances.

When I started shooting the formula, I noticed that the cannons were not strong enough to launch the formula through the atmosphere. I needed to shoot from a high point. Luckily, the only building that was tall enough to be able to shoot through the atmosphere was still standing.

When I looked towards the sky to see how much time I had left, I saw Xephermous there, just waiting. I think he was waiting for planet earth to rotate, to tell the people on the other side of the planet what would happen to them when they woke up.

That would give me an entire day to finish my plan. Then, I went running and told my friends about my plan. Everyone thought that my plan would not work, but they helped me anyway just so they could say that they gave their best effort to save the world.

We brought the cannons up to the highest point of the building. It still looked pretty far away. Alice helped me build a hydraulic mechanism to raise the cannons a little more.

Suddenly, I understood what Alice meant to say when she examined the formula. Different molecules have different properties. Maybe, if I heat up the formula and shoot it hot from the cannon, the molecules will become gaseous and rise through the atmosphere by themselves until they reach the monster.

Then, I went running back to the trash can. While I was running, by accident, I crashed into a man who was fighting with another man.

The man who I crashed into, fell to the ground, hit his head on the pavement and was knocked unconscious.

"Sorry," I said to the other man.

"No, thank you very much," he told me.

After that, I ran to the trash can and saw a lot of heat resistant plastic that I could use to build an electric pot.

I went back to the others. I built a giant electric pot. I filled the pot with the formula and heated it up. I connected some heat resistant tubes, that I also found in the trash can, to the pot. The plastic tubes sucked the hot formula inside the cannons.

I aimed straight at Xephermous.

"After this, everyone will know who I am," I told Ben.

"If it works," said Ben.

"Until never, stinky monster," I yelled as I fired the cannon.

CHAPTER SEVEN

....

THE TEST

*T*he formula shot out of the cannon.
The molecules changed from a liquid
to a gaseous state and rose through the
atmosphere. The molecules collided with
Xephermous' cheek. Xephermous only felt a
little tickle when the molecules collided
with his cheek.

"How is it still alive?" I asked.

Suddenly, I noticed that its cheek
started to turn into ashes. So, I shot again
and again.

Xephermous started to vanish.

"Whoever did this will pay dearly, you hear me!" screamed Xephermous before it vanished completely.

"That is, if we see each other again," I said.

"You saved us!" screamed Gregory.

"Really?" I asked.

"Yes, you saved us all!" screamed Alice.

"It is true," said Ben.

In situations like these, it is good to behave like a humble hero and enjoy the moment with everyone, I thought to myself.

One second later, "Ha, ha, ha! I saved the world, and you all didn't do anything! I did everything by myself because I am awesome," I said while pointing my finger at Alice, Ben, Adam, and Gregory.

Well, maybe I failed to behave like a humble hero, but at least I enjoyed the moment. Although I don't think I can say the same about them.

For the next three years, every time I saw a person on the street, I kept reminding them that I had saved them.

"Ha, ha, ha! I saved the world while you all were just crying!" I told them.

"Dr. Pren, it's driving me crazy to hear you say the same thing over and over again," said Ben.

"I am not saying the same thing over and over again, although . . . I saved the world while you were just crying," I said.

Ben was about to punch me when Adam said, "How about we change the subject? Who wants to go play video games at my house?"

"That sounds like a good idea," I said, and we went to Adam's house.

"Do you remember the 'Room of Madness'?" Adam asked me as we went by the 'Room of Madness'.

"That was a terrible experience, and every year you look more like the kid in my vision," I told Adam.

We went into Adam's room and played video games. We always liked to go to Adam's house because Ben and I didn't have video games.

Later, after playing video games, Ben and I said goodbye to Adam and left.

As we walked to our houses, Ben asked me a favor. Ben told me that he had forgotten to study for his test. Ben asked me to give him the answers to the questions for the test that he was going to have the next day.

"Yeah, but I don't know the answers either," I said.

Ben gave me a walkie talkie.

"Just look up the answers on the internet. I will give you the questions. Okay?" asked Ben.

"Yes," I said.

Once in my house, I remembered that the next day I was supposed to work on my pet that I was creating. Then, I thought, it is okay if I don't work on my pet tomorrow. I have not made great progress, anyway. Right away, I remembered that I didn't know how to use the internet. Then, I had an idea.

The next day, I woke up very early. Ben's test was at 9 in the morning, and I usually woke up at 11 in the morning. It did not feel good to interrupt my sleeping schedule, but I did it because Ben was my friend.

Before I left my house to go to Ben's school, I grabbed my favorite bread and put it in one of my sweater pockets. When I got to Ben's school, I looked for a grate that opened into the school's heating duct. I entered the school through the heating duct and started looking for Ben's class.

Finally, I found Ben's class. Since I did not know how to use the internet to find out the answers, I decided to copy the answers from another student's test.

When the test started, Ben told me the first question. I looked at the test of the student who was sitting next to Ben and gave Ben the answer that the student had written on his test.

Suddenly, I got hungry. I took my bread out of my pocket and started eating it. Bread crumbs fell on the floor while I was eating it.

Just when the time to complete the test was up, I noticed that the student who was sitting next to Ben was Adam.

"Can I please see Ben and Adam?" said the teacher while the other students went out to recess.

"Adam, why did you copy off Ben's test?" asked the teacher.

"I don't know what you are talking about," said Adam.

"Don't lie to me. You copied off Ben's test and you know it," said the teacher.

"It wasn't me, I swear," said Adam.

"You can swear all you want, but that won't change anything," said the teacher.

"You are making a big mistake," said Adam.

"Me? You are only a 9-year-old boy. I am a teacher. I know a lot more than you," said the teacher.

"I am telling you the truth," said Adam.

"Stop lying. If you don't tell me the truth, I am taking you both to the principal's office," said the teacher.

Adam was scared to death, but as the seconds went by, his fear turned into hatred.

"Are you ready to tell the truth?" asked the teacher.

"Are you ready to stop blaming me for something that I didn't do?" asked Adam.

"Stop it. I will take you to the principal's office for disrespecting me," said the teacher.

"Respect? You don't respect me at all," said Adam.

"I have had enough," said the teacher while she grabbed Adam by the arm.

"If you have had enough, imagine how I feel," said Adam.

The teacher pulled Adam by the arm to take him to the principal's office.

"Let go of me!" screamed Adam while he struggled with the teacher to let go of him.

Finally, the teacher let go of him. At that moment, Adam saw some bread crumbs on the floor. Adam recognized the bread crumbs right away. He knew that those *were crumbs from the bread that I ate every day. Immediately, Adam turned to look at Ben.*

"I was betrayed by my best friends. If I can't trust them, I can't trust anybody," said Adam.

Then, I noticed that one of Adam's eyes had turned into a snake eye. Now, Adam looked exactly like the kid in my vision.

"Not even you, Dr. Pren," said Adam.

"I think it is time to go," I said.

While I searched for the exit, I heard some screams and cries. I wanted to see what was happening. So, I climbed out of the heating duct and walked down the hall.

I saw that Adam was manipulating a bunch of things with his mind. The books were shooting out paper airplanes so hard that they knocked down everything they crashed into. The backpacks were trapping students and were locking them in the lockers. The desks were eating everything around them. The lights in the hallways were shooting electric discharges everywhere. The toilets in the bathrooms

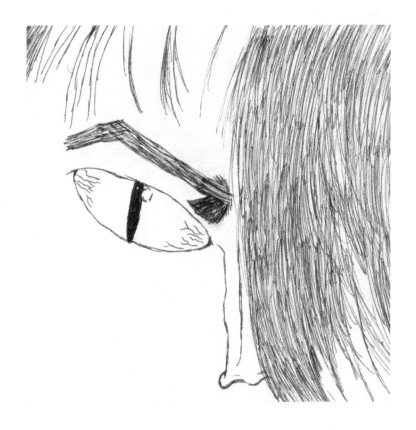

were sucking everything around them. The hallway floors were turning into quicksand.

I tried to escape, but a backpack grabbed me, picked me up in the air, and locked me in a locker. I was trapped.

"All because of a test. I should have stayed home. I could have been eating popcorn on my sofa right now," I said.

I tried to open the locker, but I couldn't. Then, I saw a skateboard next to me inside the locker. I grabbed the skateboard and started hitting the door.

Finally, the door opened. There was a little girl outside standing right in front of the locker.

"Thank you," I said as I exited the locker.

Suddenly, a desk started chasing the little girl.

The only way to end all of this was to stop the source of power, Adam.

I ran as fast as I could until I finally came out of the school. I found Ben trapped in a basketball hoop and saw Adam flying straight towards him.

"What is the matter with you?" I asked Adam.

"Finally, I understand. It seems that so much hatred made me develop supernatural powers. These powers have helped me clearly remember many things from my past. My parents are aliens. They came to planet earth because here they found more resources to survive than on their home planet. But they never imagined what I would become having been raised on a planet so different from ours," said Adam.

"The scientist you call crazy is my grandfather," said Adam.

"What!" I exclaimed.

"He pretended to be a teacher of good manners so that no one would suspect him," said Adam.

"My grandfather created the formula to destroy all human beings and thus be able to use the resources of this planet for the expansion of our civilization," said Adam.

"That was a lot of unexpected information," I said.

"This is all your fault. You are going to pay dearly for it," said Adam.

"Here is a 5-dollar bill. It is the only thing I have," I said as I put the 5-dollar bill in his hand.

Adam ripped the 5-dollar bill in half.

"Hey, you could have bought a toy with that," I said.

Then, Adam grabbed me by my shirt and lifted me into the air.

"Or maybe a piece of gum," I said.

Then, Adam threw me against a tree so hard that my head went right through the tree trunk, and my neck got stuck in the middle of the tree trunk.

"Or maybe a house. I don't know how much houses cost, but I think that is enough," I said while trying to get my head out of the tree trunk.

Then, Adam came flying towards me and pulled my head out of the tree trunk to keep fighting with me.

"Adam, you do not look happy," I said.

"I am not supposed to be happy," said Adam.

"Why not?" I asked.

"Don't call me Adam. From now on, everyone will call me Mr. Hopper," said Adam.

"So young and you already want to be an adult? Come on Adam, enjoy life while you are a kid," I said.

Ben laughed when he heard this advice coming from a kid who called himself Dr. Pren.

"If you call me Adam again, I will send an army of dolls to stop you," said Adam.

"I am not scared of dolls," I said.

"That's it. You asked for it, Dr. Pren," said Adam.

I closed my eyes and used my brilliant mind to immediately create an extraordinary plan. When I opened my eyes, I put my plan into action. Then, I slapped Adam in the face.

"I am going to tell my mom! This is not going to be the last time we see each *other!" said Adam as he cried and flew away.*

When Adam left, I went to get Ben down from the basketball hoop, but he was stuck.

Then, I had an idea. I jumped under the hoop and pushed his butt up. Ben came flying out and landed on the ground, but he was fine. So, we went to Ben's house to plan how we were going to stop Adam.

CHAPTER EIGHT

....

THE FIRES

We got to Ben's house and went straight to his bedroom. We started to talk and think of a plan to stop Adam. Two hours went by, and we still didn't have a plan.

"Come on, Dr. Pren, think of something," Ben told me.

"I've got it. We should order pizza," I said.

"Dr. Pren, concentrate!" exclaimed Ben.

"I can't think on an empty stomach," I said.

"Empty? How's that possible if you ate all my candy?" asked Ben.

"Yes, but I am still hungry," I said.

"It's okay. I have some cookies in the pantry. You can have some," said Ben.

I was excited as I headed for the pantry. Suddenly, I was paralyzed. A little doll sitting on top of the toilet in the bathroom was looking directly at me.

"Ben, you never told me that you liked dolls," I yelled.

"I don't have any dolls," said Ben as he came out of his bedroom.

Ben was paralyzed to see the doll.

"Is this a joke?" asked Ben.

"No," I said.

Suddenly, the doll got off the toilet and started to walk towards us. Every time its little feet touched the wooden floor as it walked towards us, we felt a cold and chilling breeze. You could only hear the creaking of the wooden floorboards as the doll walked.

The doll was dirty and scratched.

"Do you want to play with me?" asked the doll.

"Actually, I feel too tired to play right now," I said.

"Come on, it is a fun game. The game is called hide and seek," said the doll.

"I know what you are talking about. Actually, there are not many places to hide in this house. So, I don't think we can play hide and seek here," I said.

At that moment, the doll appeared on Ben's shoulder and kept staring at me. Ben was moving his mouth like he was trying to tell me to get the doll off his shoulder.

"If you want, I can hide first," said the doll.

"Adam sent you, right?" I asked.

"Mr. Hopper. Yes, he sent me. Are we going to play now, yes or no?" said the doll.

"No," I said.

Quickly, I grabbed the doll by the head, ran to the bathroom, threw it in the toilet, and put the toilet seat down, squashing the doll. Then, Ben and I ran off immediately.

"What did you just do?" asked Ben as we were running.

"You told me to get the doll off your shoulder," I said.

"Don't you watch movies? You should never do that to a living doll!" screamed Ben.

"Why not?" I asked.

When suddenly, the doll appeared in front of us.

"Because that makes me mad," said the doll.

I looked around to find a way to escape. The only exit was right behind the doll. Then, I realized I was in the dining room, so I grabbed a chair and hit the doll with the chair, knocking it out of the way. I opened the door, and we both ran out of the house.

"Where do we go now?" asked Ben.

"I have an idea. Today, we will spend the night at my house and tomorrow, you will

go back to your house. I never told Adam where I lived," I told Ben.

Finally, we got to my house. We went straight into my bedroom and fell asleep. That night, a commotion outside my house woke me up. I went outside to see what was going on. I couldn't believe what I was seeing.

Ben's house was burning. I quickly woke up Ben and went to his house.

"What happened?" Ben asked a neighbor.

"I don't know. Everything was turned off in the house when out of nowhere, it caught on fire. The good news is that Mr. and Mrs. Abioye were able to escape," said the neighbor.

Then, Ben and I saw his parents safe and sound. That made us really happy.

The next day, Ben told me that his family had decided to move to California.

"Why are you moving so far away?" I asked.

"Well, most of my family lives there, and my parents want me to spend more time with them," said Ben.

"When are you leaving?" I asked.

"In four hours," said Ben.

"What?" I screamed.

"We don't have anything here anymore. Our family lives far away, so we have to go now. I just wanted to say goodbye before I left," said Ben.

"Bye," I said.

"Maybe we will see each other again someday," said Ben.

"Maybe," I said.

Four hours later, I looked through my window, saw Ben get in the car, and then I saw the car drive off into the distance.

"I have a feeling that the fire was not an accident," I said to myself.

That afternoon, I went to Adam's house to figure out if Adam had something to do with the fire. I walked around to the backyard to climb the tree that led up to

Adam's bedroom. His window was always open, so it was easy to get in.

"Adam will know that I am here, so I had better hide somewhere in the house," I said.

I walked out of the bedroom and heard Adam's voice.

"If you are wondering, yes, I was the one who lit Ben's house on fire," said Adam.

I did not know what to do, so I hid in a suit of armor. Adam's dad collected many suits of armor, so I thought it would be difficult for Adam to find me if I hid in one of them. Then, I thought, what if I can't escape and I get trapped in here forever.

Then, Adam went flying right in front of me. When I saw Adam, I lost my balance, slipped inside the suit of armor, but I was able to grab ahold of the arm of the suit of armor. The arm dropped an axe that fell right behind Adam. The axe cut off the back pockets of Adam's pants. Then, I saw his underwear and could not contain my laughter.

Adam grabbed the suit of armor I was hiding in and threw it across the room. I crashed against the wall.

"That didn't feel good at all," I said.

I came out of the suit of armor quickly and jumped out of a window. I was about to touch the ground when the grass transformed into an infinite abyss. When I saw this, I grabbed onto a crack in the wall of the house and hung above the abyss.

"What a fool! The grass is not an abyss. It is an optical illusion caused by the grass' color and the angle at which you see it," said Adam as he flew towards me.

I touched the abyss with the tip of my foot and noticed that it was just grass. So, I let go of the wall and ran out onto the street.

"On the other hand, if you want a real abyss, I can create one," said Adam.

Immediately, Adam created a real infinite abyss under my feet. I grabbed onto the edge of the sidewalk just before the abyss opened up completely. Now, I was hanging from the sidewalk.

"Until never," said Adam.

When suddenly, a car crashed into Adam. Adam went flying in the air. An old grandmother got out of the car.

"Let me help you, sonny boy," said the old grandmother, and she pulled me onto the sidewalk.

"I was driving when I forgot where I was going. I accidentally crashed into your friend because I was looking for an address on my cell phone," said the grandmother.

"Thank you," I said and ran to my house.

I locked myself inside my room for the rest of the day.

During the night, a fire started in the kitchen of my house. The smoke woke me up. I came out of my bedroom and saw Adam flying through the house, leaving a trail of flames. Immediately after, Adam disappeared. I did not know how to put out the fire, so I decided to call the firefighters. But I didn't have a cell phone. Just then, I saw Mr. Thups calling the firefighters. They got to the house quickly and put out the fire.

The next day, the Thups decided to send me to live with a friend of theirs while the house was being repaired.

Their friend had three kids. They were all older than me. One was two years older than me; another was three years older than me, and the other was four years older than me. Since they lived in a small apartment, I had to share the same bedroom with the three kids. The kids were friendly, but they didn't talk to me much.

What will happen to Adam? What will my life be like from now on? I asked myself.

CHAPTER NINE

....

THE END OF THE

BEGINNING

"**W**e will leave the rest of the story for another time," said Dr. Pren.

"What do you mean we will leave the rest of the story for another time?" asked George eagerly.

"As you heard, I will not tell you anything else today. If you want to know more about my life, come back tomorrow at the same time," said Dr. Pren.

"I need you to tell me your whole life story," said George.

"Do you need to know my whole life story today?" asked Dr. Pren.

"No, but I do need to know it all by Saturday, or my life will come to an end," said George.

"Perfect. Come back tomorrow, and I will tell you more," said Dr. Pren.

"Wouldn't it be better if you went ahead and told me your whole life story today to finish sooner?" asked George.

"Many things happened to me during my life. Remember all the events that I just told you, and tomorrow I will tell you more," said Dr. Pren.

"Fine," said George disappointed as he got up from the chair.

Then, George headed towards the front door. The door opened automatically.

"How did you do that?" asked George.

"Come back tomorrow, and I will tell you. Don't worry. You will know everything about my life by Saturday," said Dr. Pren.

George left the cabin, and the door closed.

George went back to the bar.

"Well?" asked Don Ponanso.

"He didn't tell me everything about his life. Just a little part," said George.

"A little part? You spent so much time with him just to find out a little part about his life," said Don Ponanso.

"I know, but don't worry. Come back on Saturday, and I will tell you everything," said George.

Don Ponanso got up from the chair and left the bar.

George went home.

"What a day!" sighed George as he sat on his sofa.

"I wonder what Dr. Pren will tell me tomorrow," said George.

Then, George closed his eyes and fell asleep on his sofa.

TO BE CONTINUED . . .

Read all the books written by
Máximo César Castellanos

Peter: A Chapter Book

Big Foot Hunting (Book 1)

Skeleton Wars (Book 2)

The Red Goblin (Book 3)

The Ghosts in My Attic (Book 4)

The Haunted Swamp (Book 5)

Dr. Pren and the Days of his Childhood

ABOUT THE AUTHOR

Máximo was born in Delaware.
At the age of 3, Máximo began creating stories through drawings. At the age of 4, Máximo discovered comics. Once Máximo learned to read and write, he began to write chapter books. Máximo is now 11 years old. He likes to read stories, invent stories, and write stories. He also enjoys creating illustrations, comics, and short films.

CPSIA information can be obtained
at www.ICGtesting.com
Printed in the USA
LVHW080902100920
665516LV00013B/205/J

9 780578 728186